J'ai six ans

1ère Partie, Unité 4

Barbara Scanes

3

4

6

Vocabulaire

quel âge as-tu ?	how old are you?
j'ai six ans	I'm six (years old)
tu as sept ans	you're seven (years old)
tu as sept ans ?	are you seven (years old)?
c'est	it is
bientôt	soon
mon anniversaire	my birthday
en ce moment	at the moment
tu es	you are
un bébé	a baby

Luc et Sophie – a challenge

Colour in the picture and write what you think Sophie and Nadine are saying in the speech bubbles. (This page may be photocopied.)

J'ai six ans

Barbara Scanes

Luc and Sophie are at the swimming pool. Sophie introduces herself to Nadine and they find out how old they both are. Luc tries to join in the conversation. What does Sophie do?

J'ai six ans is one of the stories in *Learn French with Luc et Sophie*, a story-based scheme for teaching French in primary schools.

Full details of the scheme can be found on:
www.brilliantpublications.co.uk

ISBN-13: 978-1-78317-151-4

9 781783 171514

Brilliant
PUBLICATIONS